Remember when... Songs full of memories...

of **The War Years**

Twenty-two songs full of memories, arranged for piano, voice & guitar.

WISE PUBLICATIONS
London / New York / Paris / Sydney / Copenhagen / Madrid

Exclusive Distributors:
Music Sales Limited
8/9 Frith Street, London W1V 5TZ,
England.
Music Sales Pty Limited
120 Rothschild Avenue, Rosebery,
NSW 2018, Australia.

Order No. AM950290
ISBN 0-7119-7016-5
This book © Copyright 1998 by
Wise Publications.

Book design by Michael Bell Design.
Compiled by Peter Evans,
Peter Lavender & Jack Long.
Photographs courtesy of
The Hulton Getty Picture Collection.

Printed in the United Kingdom

Your Guarantee of Quality:
As publishers, we strive to produce every
book to the highest commercial standards.
This book has been carefully designed to
minimise awkward page turns and to
make playing from it a real pleasure.
Particular care has been given to specifying
acid-free, neutral-sized paper made from pulps
which have not been elemental chlorine bleached.
This pulp is from farmed sustainable forests and
was produced with special regard for the environment.
Throughout, the printing and binding have been
planned to ensure a sturdy, attractive publication
which should give years of enjoyment.
If your copy fails to meet our high standards,
please inform us and we will gladly replace it.

Music Sales' complete catalogue describes
thousands of titles and is available in full colour
sections by subject, direct from Music Sales Limited.
Please state your areas of interest and
send a cheque/postal order for £1.50 for
postage to: Music Sales Limited, Newmarket Road,
Bury St. Edmunds, Suffolk IP33 3YB.

Remember when...

Songs full of memories...

BLESS 'EM ALL

Words & Music by Jimmy Hughes & Frank Lake

air - man just fin-ish-ing his time, There's man - y a twirp sing - ing on, _____
rook - ie has tak - en it in, Hook line and sink - er an' all, _____
air - man has blight - ed his life, Thro' writ - ing rude words on the wall, _____
rook - ie has fell in the mud, Thro' leav - ing his horse in the stall, _____ } You'll

get no pro - mo - tion this side of the o - cean, So cheer up, my lads, Bless 'em all! _____

Bless 'em all! Bless 'em all! _____ The long and the

short and the tall; _____ Bless all the ser - geants and dou-ble-u o ones,

Bless all the corp'rals and their blink - in' sons, 'Cos we're say - ing good - bye to them all. _____ As back to their bil - lets they crawl, _____ You'll get no pro - mo - tion this side of the o - cean, So cheer up, my lads, Bless 'em all! _____ No - bo - dy knows what a twirp you've been, So cheer up, my lads, Bless 'em all! _____

D.S. 𝄋

mf

rall.

sfz

ALL OVER THE PLACE

Words by Noel Gay & Frank Eyton
Music by Noel Gay

All a-round the u-ni-verse in a-ny port of call, get-ting his fun,— the son of a gun.—

Ne-ver stay-ing ve-ry long in a-ny place at all, he's here, he's there, he's ev-'ry bloom-in' where, he's

all ov-er the place, the la-dies a-dore,— to get him a-shore,— he's

their's for a day,— and then he's a-way,— all ov-er the place. place.—

BOOGIE WOOGIE BUGLE BOY

Words & Music by Don Raye & Hughie Prince

toot did-dle ah - da toot. He blows it eight to the bar—— in "boo-gie" rhy-thm.   He

can't blow a note un-less a bass and gui-tar—— is play-in' with 'im.——

He makes the comp-'ny jump when he plays re - veil - le, he's the

boo - gie woo - gie bu - gle boy of Com-pa-ny B!——   2. He   Com-pa-ny B!——

DER FUEHRER'S FACE

Words & Music by Oliver Wallace

Ve bring der vorld new or - der,_____ Heil Hit - ler's vorld "New Or - der!"_____ Ev - 'ry - one of for - eign race, vill luff der Fueh - rer's face, ven ve bring to der vorld dis - or - der._____ Ven der

D.%. al Fine

N.C.

17

GOODNIGHT, WHEREVER YOU ARE

Words & Music by Dick Robertson, Al Hoffman & Frank Weldon

I'LL BE SEEING YOU

Music by Sammy Fain
Words by Irving Kahal

ca - rou - sel, __ The chest-nut trees, __ the wish-ing well. __ I'll   be   see-ing you __ in

ev - 'ry love - ly sum - mer's day, In   ev - 'ry-thing that's light and gay, I'll   al - ways think of

you that way. I'll find you in   the morn - ing sun. And when the night is   new,   I'll be

look-ing at   the moon, __ But I'll be see - ing   you.   you. __

23

I'LL PRAY FOR YOU

Music by Stanley Hill
Words by Roy King

LILLI MARLENE

Music by Norbert Schultze
Words by Hans Leip
English Words by Tommie Connor & Jimmy Phillips

ten - der - ly, that you lov'd me, you'd al - ways be,
lan - tern light, I'd hold you tight, we'd kiss "Good - night,"} my

Lil - li of the lamp - light, my own Lil - li Mar -

lene.

Or - ders came for sail - ing some - where ov - er there,
Rest - ing in a bil - let just be - hind the line,
all con - fined to bar - racks was
ev - en tho' we're part - ed your

more than I could bear; I knew you were wait - ing in the street, I
lips are close to mine; you wait where that lan - tern soft - ly gleams, your

heard your feet, but could not meet; } my Lil - li of the
sweet your face seems, to haunt my dreams, }

lamp - - light, my own Lil - li Mar - lene.

29

I'M GONNA GET LIT UP
(WHEN THE LIGHTS GO ON IN LONDON)

Words & Music by Hubert Gregg

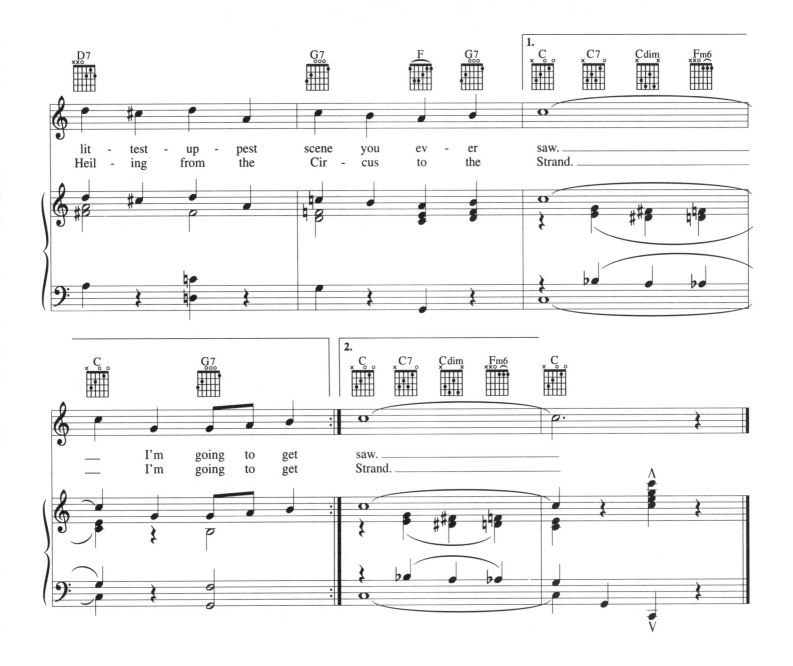

Chorus 3:
A regular flare-up when they light Trafalgar Square up,
A regular sight to open Nelson's other eye,
Through the day and through the night,
Signal beacons they will light,
"England this day expects the nation to be tight."
They'll have to stop traffic when they light Trafalgar Square up,
And down the rocky road to Westminster we'll reel, reel, reel,
What a shindy we will kick up,
Old Big Ben will chime a hiccup,
To epitomise the sentiments we feel.

Chorus 4:
I'm going to get unsedately so serenely stinking
I'm going to get stinking as I've never been before,
When the dogs have had their day,
And the fight has had its fray,
We'll all be swapping battle-dress for bottle dress that day.
I'm going to positively permanently pie-eyed,
The day we finally exterminate the Huns, Huns, Huns,
They'll be joy and they'll be laughter,
And there'll be no Morning After,
For we'll all be drunk for muns and muns and muns.

LET THE PEOPLE SING

Words by Noel Gay, Ian Grant & Frank Eyton
Music by Noel Gay

too much sad-ness a-round._____ Let mu - sic

come to our aid._____ Com - mand that mu - sic be

made._____ Let all the peo - ple pa - rade,_____

this shall be___ my de - cree.___

35

Let the peo-ple sing, sing like a-ny-thing, a-ny sort of song they choose._____ Let the peo-ple sing, let the wel-kin ring a-ny-thing to kill the blues._____ Find a mer-ry song to cheer them,_____

MISTER BROWN OF LONDON TOWN

Words & Music by R. Arkell & Noel Gay

far as he___ could see, he'd got his wife,___ he'd

got his kids___ and things were right___ as rain, un - til the God - for -

sa - ken Hun___ got bu - sy once___ a - gain. Then

Mis - ter Brown___ of Lon - don Town___ had a job___ to

things blew down,— seemed a blink - in' shame, bloom - in' fire— and

flame, bli - mey, what— a game! But who stood up— and

saved the town,— when Lon - don Bridge— was fall - ing down?— Mis - ter Brown— of

Lon - don Town.— "Oi," Mis - ter Brown!—

41

LORDS OF THE AIR

Words & Music by Michael North & Davy Burnaby

our new bat - tle - field, the sky,_____ pre - pared to do or dare_____ let
where - so - ere her sons may be,_____ o'er this our coun - try fare_____ fly

this be our new bat - tle - cry, "Brit - tan - nia rules the air."
on, fly on to vic - to - ry, "Brit - tan - nia rules the air."

CHORUS

Eng - land our is - land home,_____ land of the

mf-ff

free,_____ Eng - land un - con - quered yet_____

PRAISE THE LORD AND PASS THE AMMUNITION

Words & Music by Frank Loesser

"Praise the Lord, and pass the am-mu-ni-tion! Praise the Lord, and pass the am-mu-ni-tion!

Praise the Lord, and pass the am-mu-ni-tion and we'll all stay free!

Praise the Lord, and swing in-to po-si-tion, can't af-ford to be a po-li-ti-cian,

praise the Lord, we're all be-tween per-di-tion and the deep blue sea!" Yes, the

THE FLEET'S IN PORT AGAIN

Words & Music by Noel Gay

Brightly

Flags are fly-ing in ev-'ry street,——

bands are play-ing a stir-ring beat,——

mirth and mu - sic are in the air,____

joy and hap - pi - ness ev - 'ry - where.____

CHORUS

The fleet's____ in

port a - gain,____ back home,____ in

49

THERE'LL ALWAYS BE AN ENGLAND

Words & Music by Ross Parker & Hughie Charles

UNDERNEATH THE ARCHES

Words & Music by Bud Flanagan

Ritz I nev-er sigh for, The Carl-ton they can keep,___ There's on-ly one place
I don't en-vy oth-ers The com-forts of a home,___ For there's one place where

that I know, And that is where I sleep.)
I can rest, When I've no wish to roam.)

CHORUS
Un-der-neath the Arch - es,___

and sleep-ing when it's fine, _____ I hear the trains rat - tling by a -

bove, _____ Pave-ment is my pil - low, _____ no mat-ter where I

stray, _____ Un-der-neath the arch - es, I dream my dreams a -

way. Un-der-neath the way. _____

opt: D.%.

tacet .... *

RUN, RABBIT, RUN

Music by Noel Gay
Words by Noel Gay & Ralph Butler

63

get up ear - ly and sing this lit - tle song.
know I help 'em to dodge the rab - bit pie.

Run, rab - bit, run, rab - bit, run, run, run. Run, rab - bit,

run, rab - bit, run, run, run. Bang, bang, bang, bang,

goes the farm - er's gun, run, rab - bit, run, rab - bit, run, run,

WE'LL MEET AGAIN

Words & Music by Ross Parker & Hughie Charles

68

WHEN THE LIGHTS GO ON AGAIN
(ALL OVER THE WORLD)

Words & Music by Eddie Seiler, Sol Marcus & Bennie Benjamin

WHEN THE POPPIES BLOOM AGAIN

Words & Music by Don Pelosi, Leo Towers & Morton Morrow

The Flan-ders bat-tle-fields have known the plough,
I live in mem-o-ry of days gone by,

The corn is wav-ing and it's
When love was ev-'ry thing to

peace-ful now,
you and I;

But love un-dy-ing still keeps me sigh-ing,
I still re-mem-ber love's glow-ing em-ber,

WHEN THEY SOUND THE LAST ALL CLEAR

Words & Music by Hugh Charles & Louis Elton

clouds roll a - way, and the sun will be shin - ing a -

new._____ When they sound the last all clear,_____

CHORUS

— how hap - py my dar - ling we'll be,_____ when they

turn up the lights and the dark lone - ly nights, are on - ly a

YOU ARE MY SUNSHINE

Words & Music by Jimmie Davis & Charles Mitchell

4/06(58570)